SPOT THE
DIFFERENCE

PaRragon

Bath · New York · Singapore · Hong Kong · Cologne · Delhi
Melbourne · Amsterdam · Johannesburg · Auckland · Shenzhen

First published by Parragon in 2011

Parragon
Queen Street House
4 Queen Street
Bath
BA1 1HE, UK

Copyright © Parragon Books Ltd 2011

Design, layout and photo manipulation by
quadrum■
www.quadrumltd.com

ISBN: 978-1-4454-2024-0

Printed in China

Contents

1 BASIC 08

2 MODERATE 30

3 CHALLENGING 54

4 ADVANCED 78

5 EXTREME 104

SOLVING THE PUZZLES

1. Give yourself a minute to carefully scrutinise each of the pictures.
2. Then, start comparing them with each other.
3. Each time you spot a difference in a picture, make sure to mark it out.
4. Once you think you are done, cross check your findings with the answers provided at the back of the book.

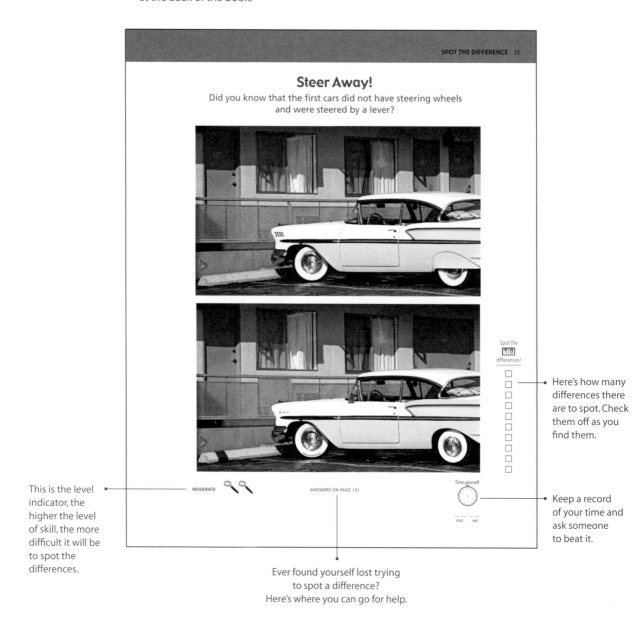

This is the level indicator, the higher the level of skill, the more difficult it will be to spot the differences.

Here's how many differences there are to spot. Check them off as you find them.

Keep a record of your time and ask someone to beat it.

Ever found yourself lost trying to spot a difference? Here's where you can go for help.

1. Take a minute to carefully scrutinise all six images.
2. Five of these pictures are exactly the same. One is just a little different.
   Can you find the odd one?
3. Don't forget to time yourself!

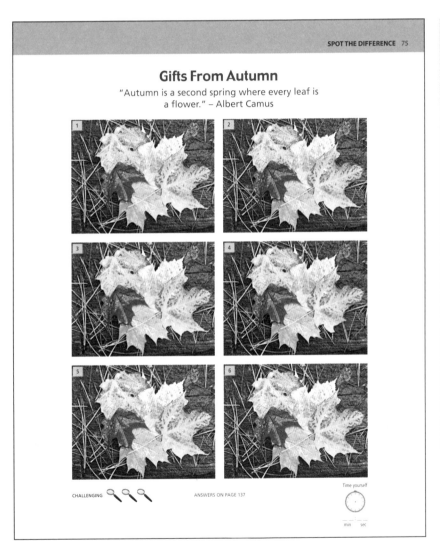

Gifts From Autumn

"Autumn is a second spring where every leaf is a flower." – Albert Camus

CHALLENGING

ANSWERS ON PAGE 137

Time yourself

min   sec

5 EXTREME

4 ADVANCED

3 CHALLENGING

2 MODERATE

1 BASIC

COLOUR CODED SECTIONS

These colour coded sections will help you identify the level of difficulty. So keep going up the elevator by challenging yourself to master these five levels.

Happy Spotting...

BASIC

Calling all ye rookies and veterans, young and old: Try these puzzles and see how good you actually are.

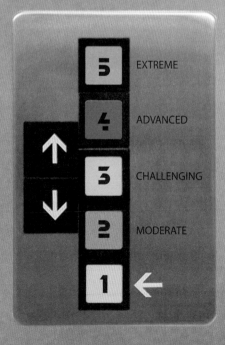

5 EXTREME

4 ADVANCED

3 CHALLENGING

2 MODERATE

1

Giddy-up Fellas!

In 1898, a group of cowboys fought the Spanish-American war under the leadership of Teddy Roosevelt as the famous 'Rough Riders'.

BASIC

Spot the

differences!

ANSWERS ON PAGE 128

Time yourself

__ __ : __ __
min   sec

Music For Your Soul

"Music can change the world because it can change people." – Bono

Spot the

differences!

BASIC

ANSWERS ON PAGE 128

Time yourself

__ __ : __ __
min   sec

A Pair Of Cows

Did you know that cows can detect a smell from five miles away?

Spot the

0 8

differences!

☐
☐
☐
☐
☐
☐
☐
☐

BASIC

ANSWERS ON PAGE 128

Time yourself

__ __ : __ __
min   sec

Heaven On Earth!

"The sea, once it casts its spell, holds one in its net of wonder forever." – Jacques Yves Cousteau

Spot the

differences!

Time yourself

__ __ : __ __
min   sec

A Splash Of Colour!

Look at how much fun this little girl has had with all these colours,
Can you spot the differences below?

Spot the
1 0
differences!

Time yourself

___ : ___
min   sec

Heavenly Abode

The ceiling of the Sistine Chapel was painted by Michelangelo.

BASIC

Spot the
0 7
differences!

☐
☐
☐
☐
☐
☐
☐

BASIC

ANSWERS ON PAGE 128

Time yourself

_ _ : _ _
min   sec

Say Cheese!

"We worry about what a child will become tomorrow,
yet we forget that he is someone today." – Stacia Tauscher

Spot the

differences!

ANSWERS ON PAGE 129

Time yourself

_ _ : _ _
min   sec

Fishy Business!

The largest catfish to ever be caught was nearly nine feet long.

Spot the
0 7
differences!

☐
☐
☐
☐
☐
☐
☐

Time yourself

min : sec

BASIC

ANSWERS ON PAGE 129

Knock Knock!

The first ever pyramid built was built in Egypt in 2600 BC.
It had 15 doors but only one could open!

BASIC

ANSWERS ON PAGE 129

Time yourself

__ : __
min   sec

Quack Quack!

The Mallard Duck is the most common wild duck in the U.S.

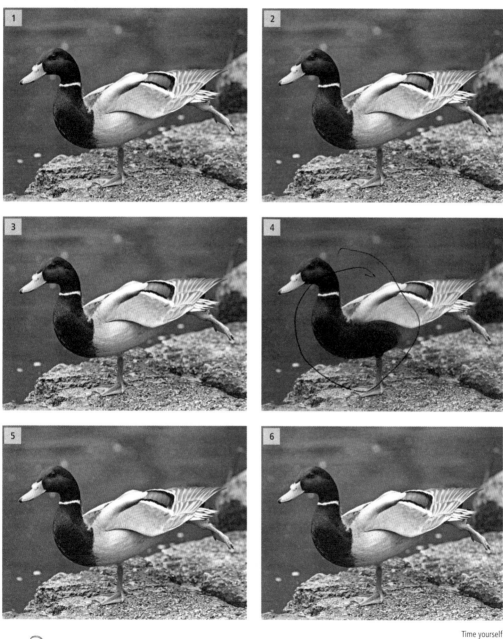

ANSWERS ON PAGE 129

Time yourself

__ __ : __ __
min   sec

Pretty Sea Shells!

The hobby of collecting and classifying shells is known as conchology.

Spot the
0 7
differences!

Time yourself

___ : ___
min   sec

Yee-Hah!

The golden age of cowboys lasted for 19 years – from 1867 to 1886!

Spot the

differences!

☐
☐
☐
☐
☐
☐

Time yourself

_ _ : _ _
min   sec

Birds Of A Feather Flock Together!
Look at these birds all perched in a row, can you spot the differences?

Spot the
0 6
differences!

☐
☐
☐
☐
☐
☐

BASIC

ANSWERS ON PAGE 130

__ : ___
min   sec

Roll Away!

Did you know that it is easier to find gold than to win
a major state lottery?

Spot the

differences!

BASIC   ANSWERS ON PAGE 130

Time yourself

__ : __
min   sec

Sun And Sand For The Soul!

Lovina Beach in Bali is made of black sand, making it a popular attraction for tourists!

Spot the

differences!

BASIC

ANSWERS ON PAGE 130

Time yourself

min   sec

Strike Out!

Did you know that three strikes in a row is called a turkey?

Spot the
0 8
differences!

☐
☐
☐
☐
☐
☐
☐
☐

BASIC

ANSWERS ON PAGE 130

Time yourself

__ __ : __ __
min   sec

Easter Delights!

Did you know that the first chocolate eggs were made in Europe in the early 19th century?

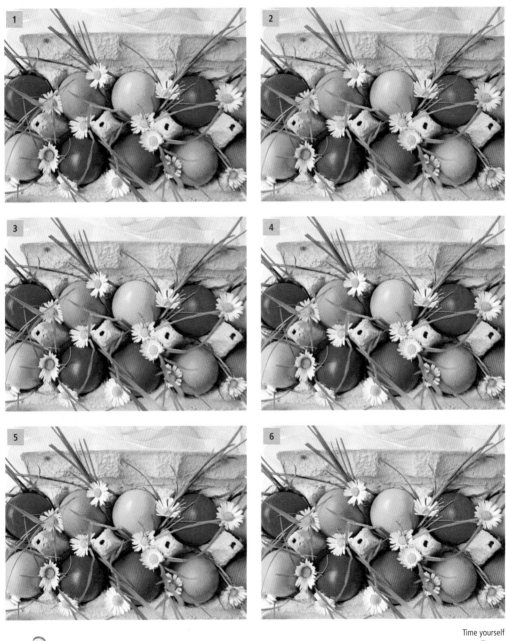

Beautiful Architecture!

"An important work of architecture will
create polemics." – Richard Meier

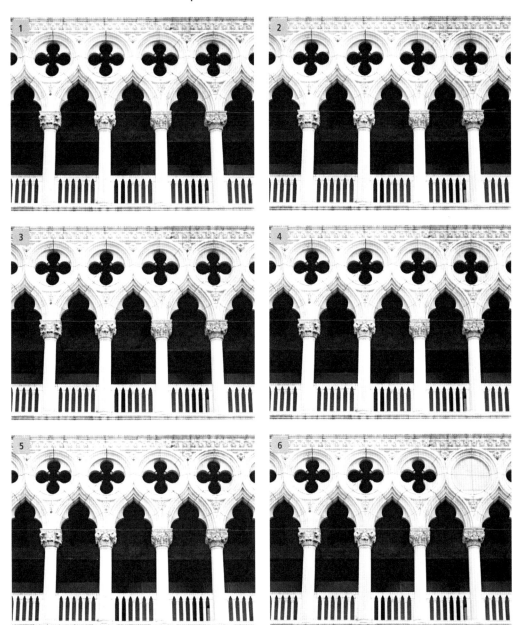

ANSWERS ON PAGE 130

Time yourself

__ __ : __ __
min   sec

MODERATE

Now that you have figured out what to do, try your hand at these slightly tougher puzzles.

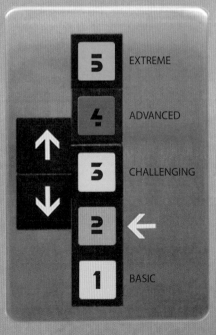

5 EXTREME

4 ADVANCED

3 CHALLENGING

2 ←

1 BASIC

Criss-Cross!

Can you find all the differences between these two pictures?

MODERATE

Spot the
0 9
differences!

☐
☐
☐
☐
☐
☐
☐
☐
☐

MODERATE

ANSWERS ON PAGE 131

Time yourself

_ _ : _ _
min   sec

A Happy Family

Can you find all the differences between these two pictures?

Spot the

differences!

Time yourself

__ : __
min   sec

Waiting To Fly Away!

Did you know that puffins can flap their wings
300 to 400 times a minute?

Spot the
0 5
differences!

MODERATE

ANSWERS ON PAGE 131

Time yourself

__ __ : __ __
min   sec

Squeaky Clean!

The world's largest bathroom is situated in
the Middle Kingdom, Egypt.

Spot the

0 7

differences!

Steer Away!

Did you know that the first cars did not have steering wheels and were steered by a lever?

Spot the
1 0
differences!

 **MODERATE**

ANSWERS ON PAGE 131

Time yourself

___ : ___
min   sec

A Stitch In Time Saves More Than Nine!

"Colours, like features, follow the changes of emotions." – Pablo Picasso

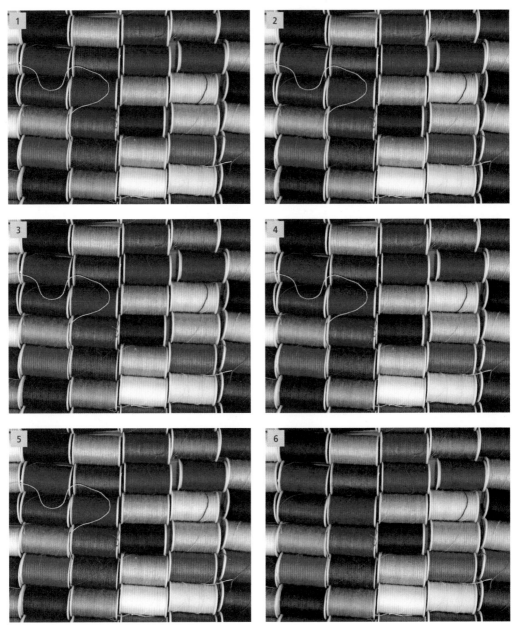

MODERATE

ANSWERS ON PAGE 131

Time yourself

__ __ : __ __
min   sec

We All Fall Down

"The fall of a leaf is a whisper to the living." – Russian Proverb

MODERATE

ANSWERS ON PAGE 132

Time yourself

__ __ : __ __
min   sec

Vacationing In Vegas!

The iconic Las Vegas sign was built in 1959 and
designed by Betty Willis.

Spot the
1 0
differences!

Scaling Profits

The New York Stock Exchange trading area is almost two thirds the size of a football field!

Spot the
0 8
differences!

MODERATE  ANSWERS ON PAGE 132

Time yourself

min   sec

A Refreshing Swim!

Ducks have no blood vessels or nerves in their feet, so they can't feel cold even in freezing water!

Spot the

differences!

ANSWERS ON PAGE 132

MODERATE

Time yourself

__ __ : __ __
min   sec

Time For Sports!

Sports is an important part of life for most people.
Can you find all the differences below?

Spot the
0 9
differences!

MODERATE   ANSWERS ON PAGE 132

Time yourself

_ _ : _ _
min   sec

On The Shores Of Justice

The national flag of the U.S. was designed by replicating George Washington's family coat of arms!

MODERATE

Spot the
0 9
differences!

☐
☐
☐
☐
☐
☐
☐
☐
☐

MODERATE

ANSWERS ON PAGE 132

Time yourself

_ _ : _ _
min   sec

Shade And Sunshine!

Nothing feels as relaxing as taking a quick swim on
a hot summer day.

Spot the

0 9

differences!

MODERATE

ANSWERS ON PAGE 133

Time yourself

__ : __
min   sec

Picture Perfect

"A family in harmony will prosper in everything." – Chinese Proverb

Spot the
0 7
differences!

☐
☐
☐
☐
☐
☐
☐

MODERATE

ANSWERS ON PAGE 133

Time yourself

__ __ : __ __
min   sec

All Rolled Up!

One of China's greatest inventions was paper in 105 AD.

Spot the
0 8
differences!

MODERATE

ANSWERS ON PAGE 133

Time yourself

— — : — —
min   sec

Slip, Slide, Splash!

The Black Hole Slide in Austria claims to be the
longest water slide in the world.

Spot the
0 7
differences!

MODERATE

ANSWERS ON PAGE 133

Time yourself

_ _ : _ _ _
min   sec

A Basket Of Fun!

Let's see if you can find the odd one out from the pictures below.

Time yourself

__ __ : __ __
min   sec

A Pasty Arrangement!

"Man needs colour to live; it's just as necessary an element as fire and water." – Fernand Leger

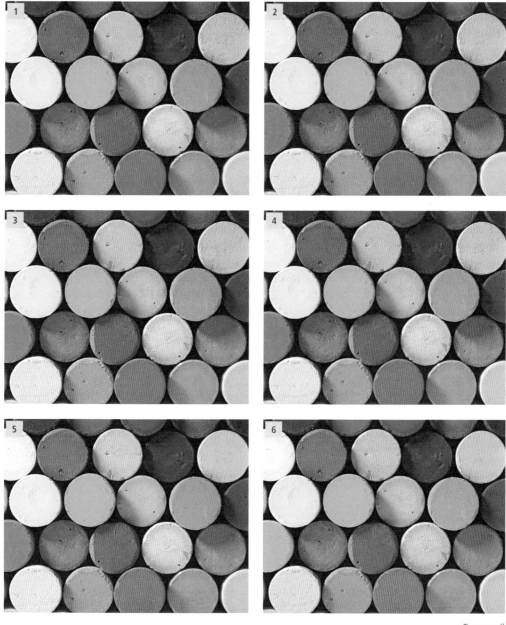

MODERATE

ANSWERS ON PAGE 133

Time yourself

___ : ___
min   sec

Ready, Set, Go!

Look at these runners all set to race. Can you spot the differences between these pictures?

Spot the
06
differences!

☐
☐
☐
☐
☐
☐

MODERATE

ANSWERS ON PAGE 134

Time yourself

__ __ : __ __
min   sec

Snowy Greetings!

Did you know that 'Jingle Bells', the most popular Christmas song, was actually written for Thanksgiving?

Spot the

differences!

☐
☐
☐
☐
☐
☐
☐

MODERATE

ANSWERS ON PAGE 134

Time yourself

__ __ : __ __
min   sec

CHALLENGING

Now the going gets tough! Time to pit your brains against our latest challenges.

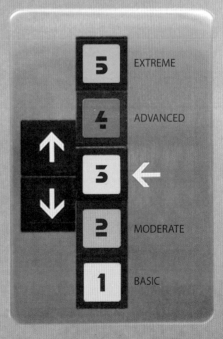

5 EXTREME

4 ADVANCED

3

2 MODERATE

1 BASIC

Rising High

Monument Valley was featured in Metallica's 'I Disappear' video!

CHALLENGING

Spot the
0 8
differences!

☐
☐
☐
☐
☐
☐
☐
☐

CHALLENGING

ANSWERS ON PAGE 134

Time yourself

__ __ : __ __
min   sec

A Land Of Many Religions

Khajuraho in Central India has the largest group of medieval Hindu and Jain temples.

Spot the
0 9
differences!

CHALLENGING

ANSWERS ON PAGE 134

Time yourself

min   sec

A Royal Ride!

Did you know that Turin is considered to be the
Baroque capital of the world?

Spot the
1 0
differences!

CHALLENGING

ANSWERS ON PAGE 134

Time yourself

_ _ : _ _
min   sec

Rocky Maze!

Stonehenge is one of the most ancient monuments in the world,
constructed between 3100 to 1100 BC.

Spot the
0 6
differences!

☐
☐
☐
☐
☐
☐

CHALLENGING    ANSWERS ON PAGE 134

Time yourself

__ : __
min   sec

Cherish The Years Of Innocence And Freedom!

"Children need models rather than critics." – Joseph Joubert

ANSWERS ON PAGE 135

CHALLENGING

Spot the
0 7
differences!

Time yourself

__ __ : __ __
min   sec

Ready To Paint

The bristles close to the handle of a paintbrush are called belly.

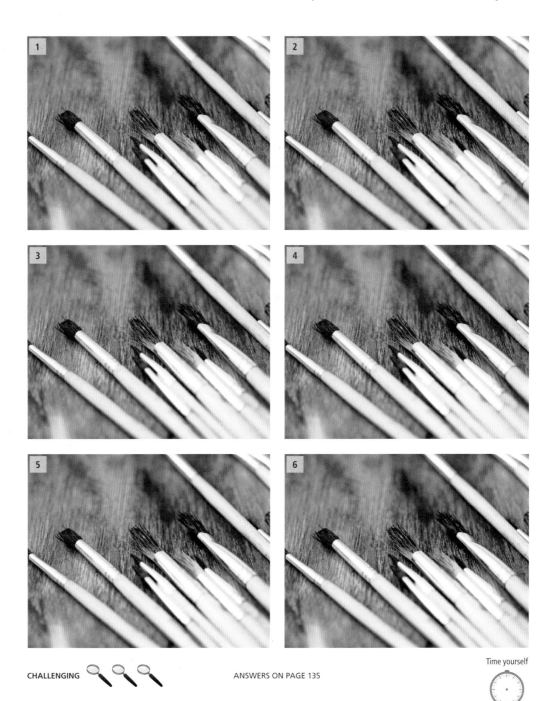

CHALLENGING

ANSWERS ON PAGE 135

Time yourself

— — : — —
min   sec

Colours Of Christmas!

Did you know that the candle industry is the fastest growing industry today?

ANSWERS ON PAGE 135

Time yourself

__ : __
min   sec

Artistically Ruined

Did you know that the Parthenon in Athens is considered to be the finest example of Doric style construction?

Spot the

differences!

Time yourself

__ __ : __ __
min   sec

Artistic Expressions

Vincent Van Gogh painted approximately 500 paintings
in a period of 10 years!

CHALLENGING

ANSWERS ON PAGE 135

Time yourself

min   sec

Colourful Flight!

Can you spot all the differences between the two pictures?

Spot the

differences!

CHALLENGING

ANSWERS ON PAGE 135

Time yourself

_ _ : _ _
min   sec

Heaven Sent!

Coconut trees can help us in so many ways! By burning the husk,
you can create a mosquito repellent!

Spot the
0 7
differences!

CHALLENGING

ANSWERS ON PAGE 136

Time yourself

min   sec

All Stacked Up!

Can you spot all the differences below?

Spot the  differences!

Time yourself

—— : ——
min   sec

Land Ahoy!

Did you know that the bathroom on a boat is called a head?

Spot the
0 7
differences!

☐
☐
☐
☐
☐
☐
☐

CHALLENGING

ANSWERS ON PAGE 136

Time yourself

___ : ___
min sec

Enter A World Of Colourful Dreams!

Did you know that within 10 minutes of waking up,
you tend to forget 90% of your dream?

Spot the
08
differences!

CHALLENGING

ANSWERS ON PAGE 136

Time yourself

__ : __
min   sec

Birthday Treat!

Did you know that the most common birth date
in the U.S. is 5th October?

Spot the
07
differences!

CHALLENGING

ANSWERS ON PAGE 136

Time yourself

__ __ : __ __
min   sec

A Beautiful Garden

"Gardening requires a lot of water, mostly in the form
of perspiration." – Lou Erickson

CHALLENGING

Spot the
09
differences!

☐
☐
☐
☐
☐
☐
☐
☐
☐

CHALLENGING

ANSWERS ON PAGE 136

Time yourself

__ __ : __ __
min   sec

Pastalicious Delight!

There are more than 600 shapes of pasta produced
all over the world!

Spot the

differences!

☐
☐
☐
☐
☐
☐
☐
☐
☐

CHALLENGING  ANSWERS ON PAGE 137

Time yourself

__ __ : __ __
min sec

Premiere Night!

Popcorn was first served in movie theatres in 1912.

Spot the

differences!

CHALLENGING

ANSWERS ON PAGE 137

Time yourself

__ __ : __ __
min   sec

Finger Painting!

Look at all the pretty colours and the sweet smile,
can you also spot the one that is different?

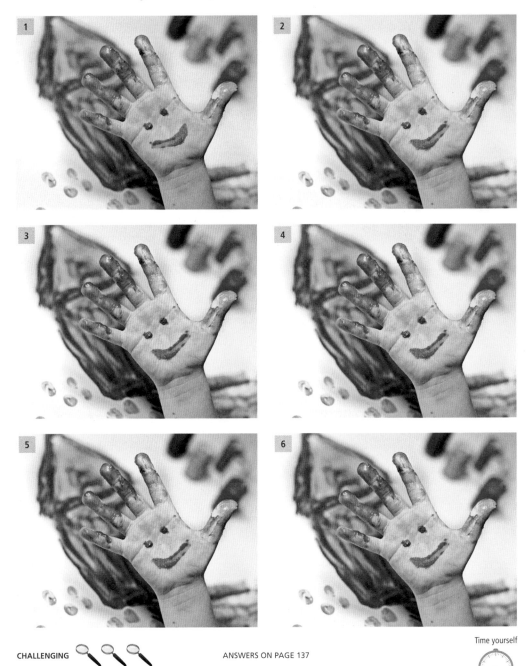

CHALLENGING

ANSWERS ON PAGE 137

Time yourself

_ _ : _ _
min   sec

Gifts From Autumn

"Autumn is a second spring where every leaf is a flower." – Albert Camus

Time yourself

__ : __
min   sec

ADVANCED

Kudos on cracking the earlier puzzles. Now is your chance to raise the bar further.

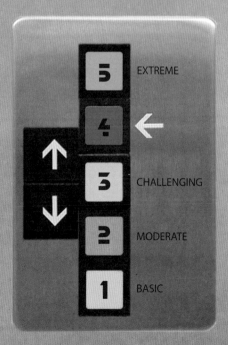

5 EXTREME

4

3 CHALLENGING

2 MODERATE

1 BASIC

Where The Earth Meets The Sky

The Sears Tower's observation deck is one of Chicago's most popular attractions as well as its highest observatory!

ADVANCED

Spot the
1 0
differences!

ADVANCED  ANSWERS ON PAGE 137

Time yourself

__ __ : __ __
min   sec

Feast To Your Heart's Content!

Candy floss was invented in 1897 by William Morris and
John Wharton in Tennessee. It was originally called 'fairy floss'.

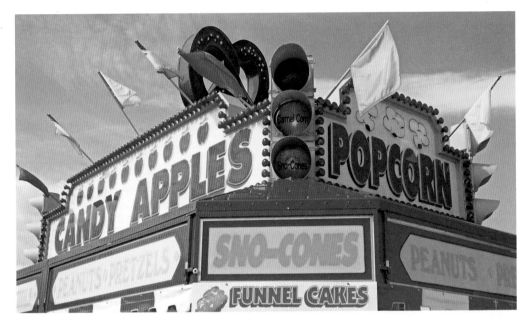

Spot the
0 8
differences!

ADVANCED

ANSWERS ON PAGE 137

Time yourself

__ __ : __ __
min   sec

Nature's Fragrant Gifts!

"Gather the flowers, but spare the buds." – Andrew Marvell

Spot the
0 9
differences!

- [ ]
- [ ]
- [ ]
- [ ]
- [ ]
- [ ]
- [ ]
- [ ]
- [ ]

ADVANCED

ANSWERS ON PAGE 138

Time yourself

__ __ : __ __
min   sec

Soothing Falls!

Cascata Delle Marmore in Italy is the tallest man-made
waterfall in the world!

Spot the
10
differences!

☐
☐
☐
☐
☐
☐
☐
☐
☐
☐

 ADVANCED   ANSWERS ON PAGE 138

Time yourself

__ __ : __ __
min   sec

Arriving Soon!

Chicago's O'Hare International Airport handles more than
75 million people on a yearly basis!

Spot the
0 8
differences!

Time yourself

min   sec

Sunshine Yellow!

Isn't it amazing how easily a brightly coloured flower
can brighten up your day? Spot the different flowers here!

ADVANCED    ANSWERS ON PAGE 138

Time yourself

__ : __
min   sec

Measuring Up!

A measuring tape can even measure curves and corners
due to its flexibility.

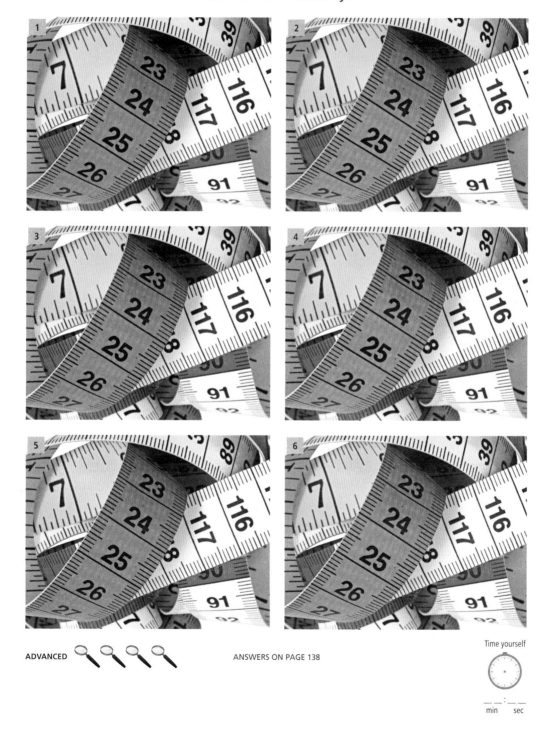

ADVANCED

ANSWERS ON PAGE 138

Time yourself

___ : ___
min   sec

Let's Play Ball!

The National Football League in America was established in 1921.
See if you can spot the differences between these players.

Spot the
0 8
differences!

ADVANCED

ANSWERS ON PAGE 138

Time yourself

_ _ : _ _
min   sec

A Swarm Of Bees

During midsummer, a healthy beehive can be inhabited by up to 80,000 bees, but only one queen bee.

Spot the
09
differences!

ADVANCED

ANSWERS ON PAGE 139

Time yourself

___ : ___
min   sec

Gear Up!

Safety gear is important in any risky job. There's no risk in finding out the differences in the pictures below.

Spot the

differences!

☐
☐
☐
☐
☐
☐
☐
☐
☐

ADVANCED

ANSWERS ON PAGE 139

Time yourself

__ __ : __ __
min   sec

Mooving On

Before the invention of milking machines in 1894,
farmers could milk only six cows per hour.

Spot the

0 8

differences!

☐
☐
☐
☐
☐
☐
☐
☐

ADVANCED   ANSWERS ON PAGE 139

Time yourself

__ __ : __ __
min   sec

Home Sweet Home!

Can you spot the differences between these pictures
of this beautiful home?

ADVANCED

Spot the
1 0
differences!

☐
☐
☐
☐
☐
☐
☐
☐
☐
☐

ADVANCED

ANSWERS ON PAGE 139

Time yourself

_ _ : _ _
min   sec

Spread Some Smiles!

See if you can spot the differences between this cheery bunch.

Spot the
0 7
differences!

☐
☐
☐
☐
☐
☐
☐

ADVANCED ANSWERS ON PAGE 139

Time yourself

__ __ : __ __
min   sec

A Healthy Sight!

Did you know that the tomato is actually a fruit
and not a vegetable?

Spot the

differences!

☐
☐
☐
☐
☐
☐
☐
☐

ADVANCED

ANSWERS ON PAGE 139

Time yourself

__ __ : __ __
min   sec

The Shores Of Civilisation!

The world's first skyscraper, the Home Insurance Company,
was built in Chicago in 1885.

Spot the

0 9

differences!

All For One And One For All!

"The difference between a helping hand and an outstretched palm is a twist of the wrist." – Laurence Leamer

Spot the
0 9
differences!

ADVANCED

ANSWERS ON PAGE 140

Time yourself

—— : ——
min   sec

Pegged Down!

The first patented clothes peg was issued in March 1832.

ADVANCED

ANSWERS ON PAGE 140

Time yourself

__ __ : __ __
min   sec

Walls Of Stone!

"A rolling stone gathers no moss, but it gains
a certain polish." – Oliver Herford

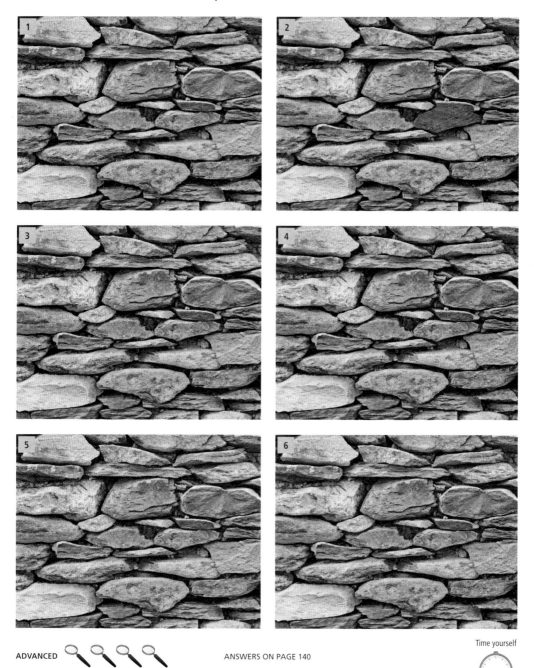

ADVANCED

ANSWERS ON PAGE 140

Time yourself

__ __ : __ __
min   sec

Aim For The Sky!

The National Mall has served as a gathering place in the
U.S. for over 200 years!

ADVANCED

Spot the
1 0
differences!

☐
☐
☐
☐
☐
☐
☐
☐
☐
☐

ADVANCED

ANSWERS ON PAGE 140

Time yourself

__ __ : __ __
min   sec

Health With A Smile!

Fruits and vegetables can act as powerful antioxidants, protecting the body against harmful free radicals and certain diseases.

Spot the

differences!

 **ADVANCED**   ANSWERS ON PAGE 140

Time yourself

__ __ : __ __
min   sec

All Aboard!

Did you know that the largest station in the world is Grand Central in New York? It has 44 platforms!

Spot the
10
differences!

ADVANCED    ANSWERS ON PAGE 141

Time yourself

_ _ : _ _
min   sec

EXTREME

Hurray, you're almost a grand master...if you crack a few more, you're the best!

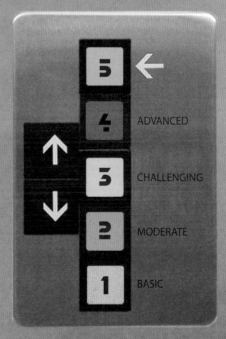

5 ←

4   ADVANCED

3   CHALLENGING

2   MODERATE

1   BASIC

Standing Tall

Doesn't that look like a bustling city? Spot the differences between the two pictures.

EXTREME

Spot the
0 7
differences!

☐
☐
☐
☐
☐
☐
☐

Time yourself

__ __ : __ __
min   sec

Christmas Joy!

Children across the globe look forward to receiving presents at Christmas.

Spot the

differences!

A Breathtaking Sight

Did you know that some of the highest mountains in the world are actually at the bottom of the sea?

Spot the
0 6
differences!

☐
☐
☐
☐
☐
☐

EXTREME   ANSWERS ON PAGE 141

Time yourself

__ __ : __ __
min   sec

Fresh From The Field!

Did you know that almost 24 million people in the
U.S. are employed in agriculture?

Spot the

differences!

It's A Rich Man's World!

Did you know that the average life of a dollar bill is just 18 months?

Spot the
0 7
differences!

EXTREME

ANSWERS ON PAGE 141

Time yourself

__ : __
min   sec

Seashells Seashells On The Seashore!

Seashells have been admired, studied and used by humans for many different purposes throughout history

EXTREME

ANSWERS ON PAGE 142

Time yourself

—— : ——
min   sec

Pretty Wings!

Did you know that butterflies can taste with their feet?

EXTREME

ANSWERS ON PAGE 142

Time yourself

__ __ : __ __
min   sec

Knock, Knock, Knocking On Many Doors!

"All doors open to courtesy." – Thomas Fuller

EXTREME

Spot the
10
differences!

☐
☐
☐
☐
☐
☐
☐
☐
☐
☐

EXTREME

ANSWERS ON PAGE 142

Time yourself

_ _ : _ _
min   sec

Missouri Beckons!

St. Louis was founded in 1964 – just south of where
the rivers, Mississippi and Missouri met.

Spot the

differences!

EXTREME

ANSWERS ON PAGE 142

Time yourself

__ __ : __ __
min   sec

Dinner On The Sidewalk!

The term 'restaurant' was first used in France during the 16th century, to mean 'a food which restores'.

Spot the

differences!

EXTREME

ANSWERS ON PAGE 142

Time yourself

__ __ : __ __
min   sec

If Only Every Car Park Was So Empty!

Can you spot the differences between these two photos?

Spot the

differences!

Time yourself

__ : __ __
min   sec

The Nation's Guardians

Mount Rushmore covers 1,278.45 acres (5.17 km²)
and is 5,725 feet (1,745 m) above sea level.

Spot the

0 6

differences!

EXTREME

ANSWERS ON PAGE 143

Time yourself

___ : ___
min   sec

Fashionista!

Seventh Avenue is known as Fashion Avenue as it is the centre of the fashion industry in New York City.

Spot the

differences!

Time yourself

__ : __
min   sec

Precious Collections

The world's first postage stamp was called the Penny Black and first went into use in the UK in 1840.

Spot the
0 7
differences!

EXTREME

ANSWERS ON PAGE 143

Time yourself

___ : ___
min   sec

A Rocky Adventure!

"Faith moves mountains, but you need to push while you pray." – Mason Cooley

EXTREME

Spot the
0 8
differences!

☐
☐
☐
☐
☐
☐
☐
☐

EXTREME

ANSWERS ON PAGE 143

Time yourself

_ _ : _ _
min   sec

Stuck Again!

Waste some time the next time you're in a jam and spot the differences in these two pictures.

Spot the

differences!

 EXTREME

ANSWERS ON PAGE 143

Time yourself

__ __ : __ __
min   sec

Paradise In The Form Of St. Tropez!

St. Tropez was fairly unknown around the world until celebrities
made it popular in the 1960s.

Spot the
0 9
differences!

EXTREME

ANSWERS ON PAGE 143

Time yourself

__ __ : __ __
min   sec

Oui, Paris

Paris is one of the most popular tourist destinations in the world, attracting 45 million visitors a year.

Spot the

differences!

EXTREME 　ANSWERS ON PAGE 144

Time yourself

___ : ___
min   sec

Dig In To A Delightful Salad!

Did you know that lettuce is a member of the sunflower family?

Spot the
0 9
differences!

☐
☐
☐
☐
☐
☐
☐
☐
☐

Time yourself

___ : ___
min   sec

EXTREME   ANSWERS ON PAGE 144

Let's Make Some Music!

The cello, the bass viol and the viola are all members
of the violin family.

EXTREME

ANSWERS ON PAGE 144

Time yourself

__ __ : __ __
min   sec

A Starry Treat!

"Cookies are made of butter and love." – A Norwegian Proverb

EXTREME

ANSWERS ON PAGE 144

Time yourself

__ __ : __ __
min   sec

Page 09:

Page 10:

Page 11:

Page 12:

Page 13:

Page 15:

Page 16:

Page 17:

Page 18:

Page 19:

Page 20:

Page 21:

Page 22:

Page 23:

Page 24:

Page 25:

Page 26:

Page 27:

Page 31:

Page 32:

Page 33:

Page 34:

Page 35:

Page 36:

Page 37:

Page 38:

Page 39:

Page 40:

Page 41:

Page 43:

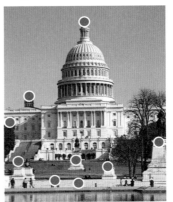

Page 44:

Page 45:

Page 46:

Page 47:

Page 48:

Page 49:

Page 50:

Page 51:

Page 55:

Page 56:

Page 57:

Page 58:

Page 59:

Page 60:

Page 61:

Page 62:

Page 63:

Page 64:

Page 65:

Page 66:

Page 67:

Page 68:

Page 69:

Page 71:

Page 72:

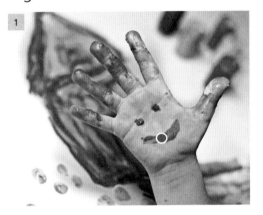

Page 73:

Page 74:

Page 75:

Page 79:

Page 80:

Page 81:

Page 82:

Page 83:

Page 84:

Page 85:

Page 86:

Page 87:

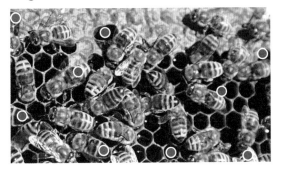

Page 88:

Page 89:

Page 91:

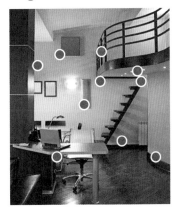

Page 92:

Page 93:

Page 94:

Page 95:

Page 96:

Page 97:

Page 99:

Page 100:

Page 101:

Page 105:

Page 106:

Page 107:

Page 108:

Page 109:

Page 110:

Page 111:

Page 113:

Page 114:

Page 115:

Page 116:

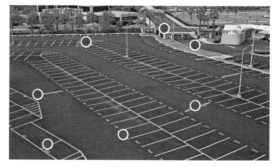

Page 117:

Page 118:

Page 119:

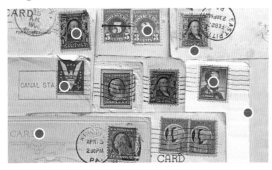

Page 121:

Page 122:

Page 123:

Page 124:

Page 125:

Page 126:

Page 127: